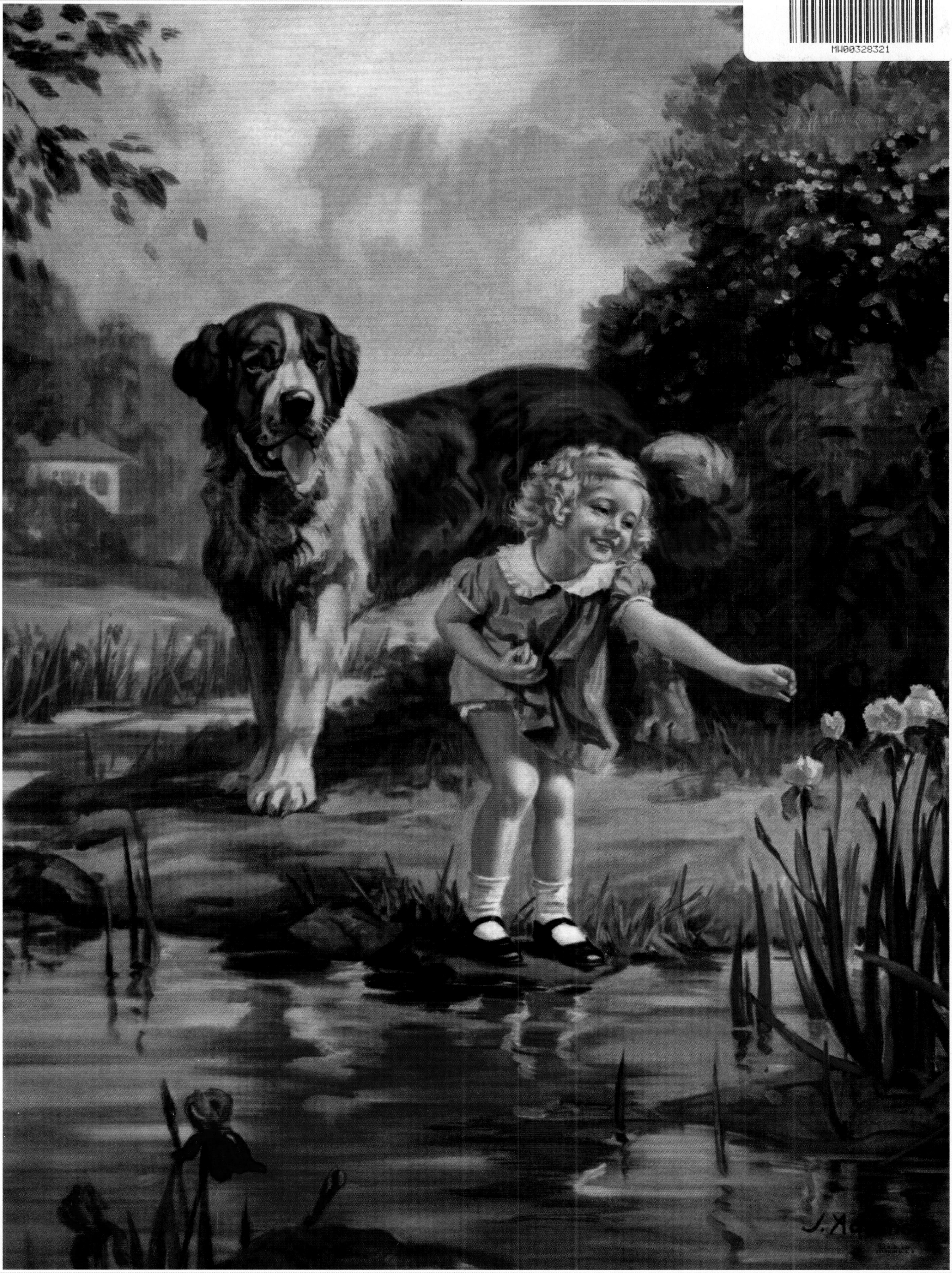

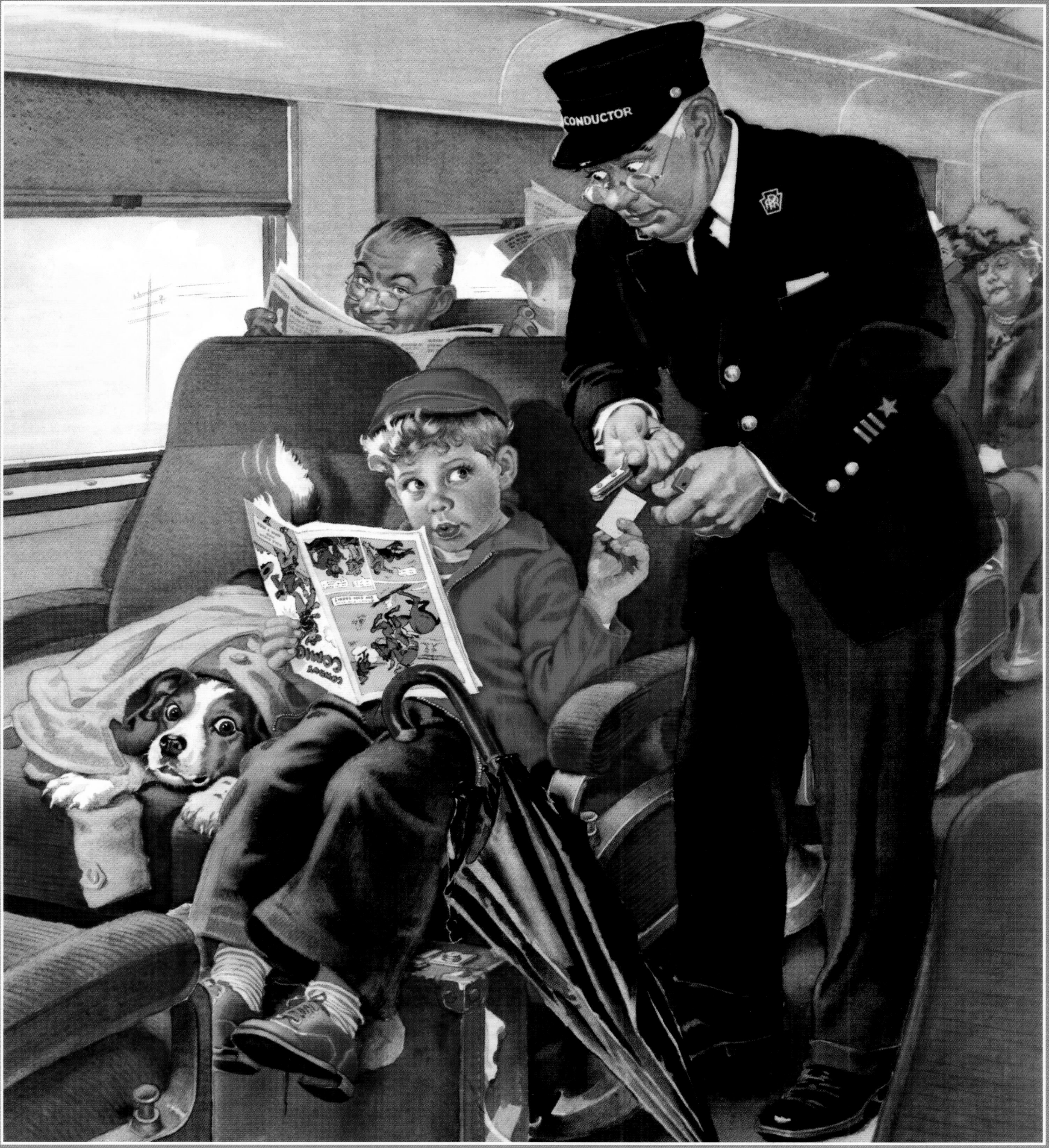
CONDUCTOR

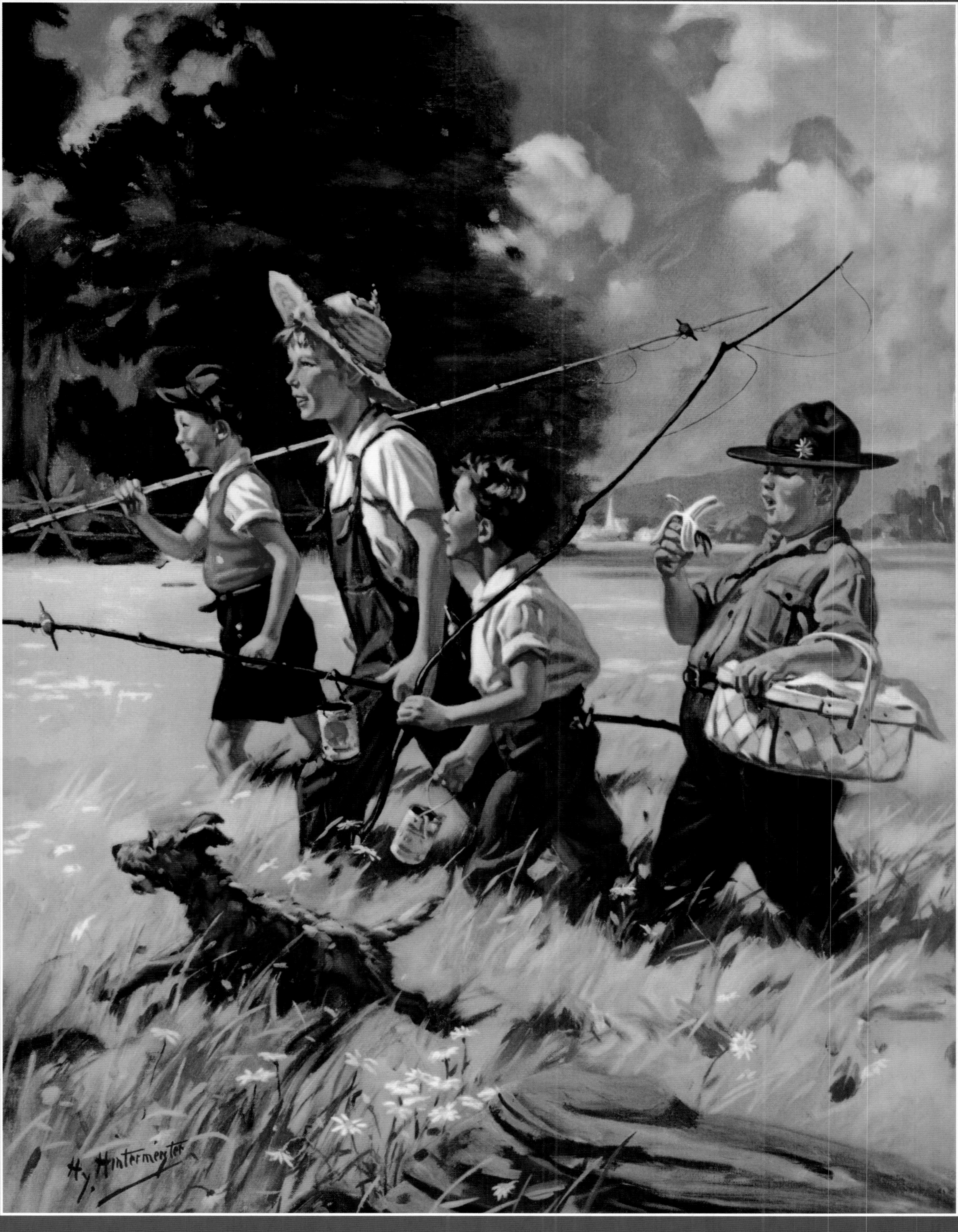
Hy. Hintermeister

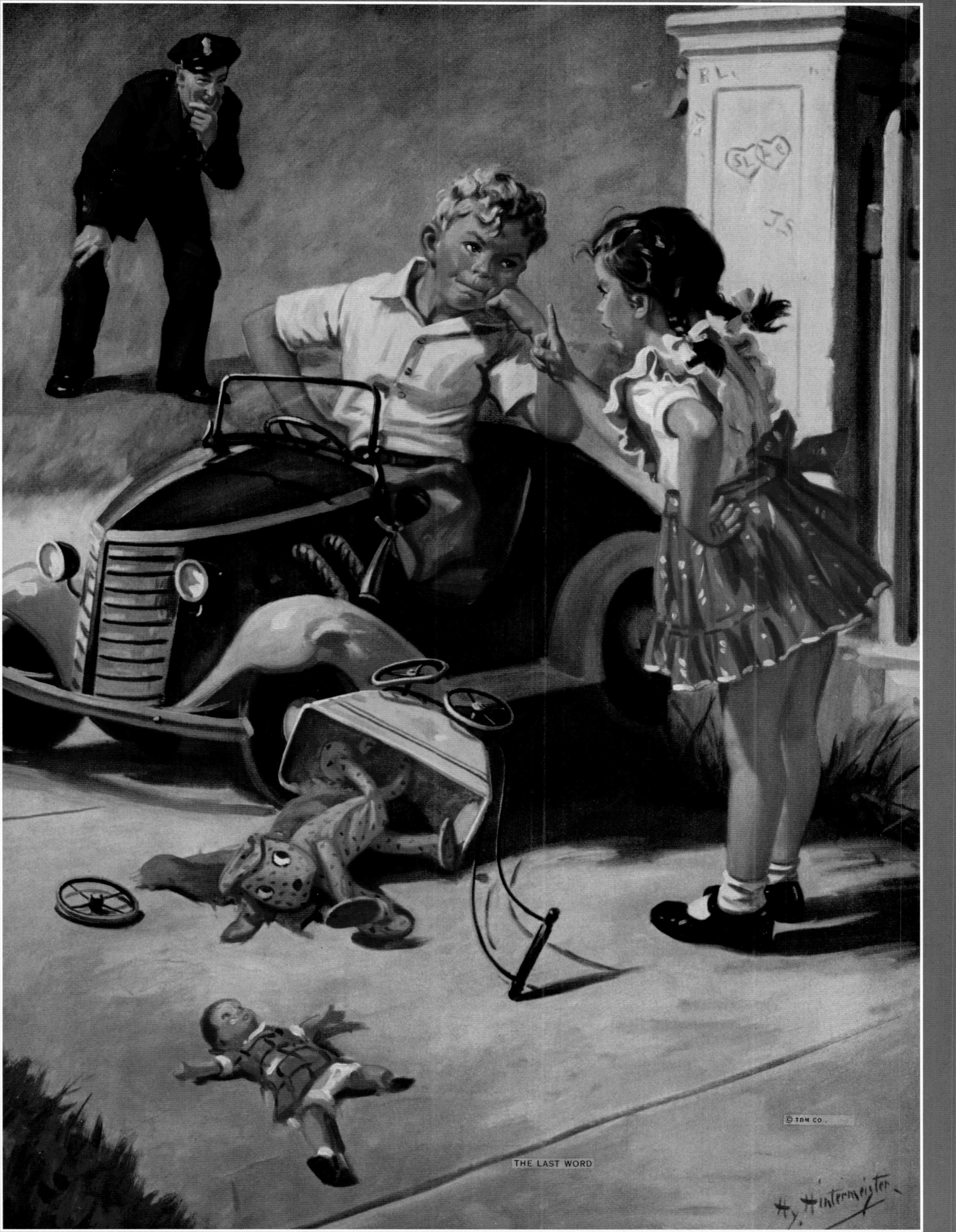

THE LAST WORD

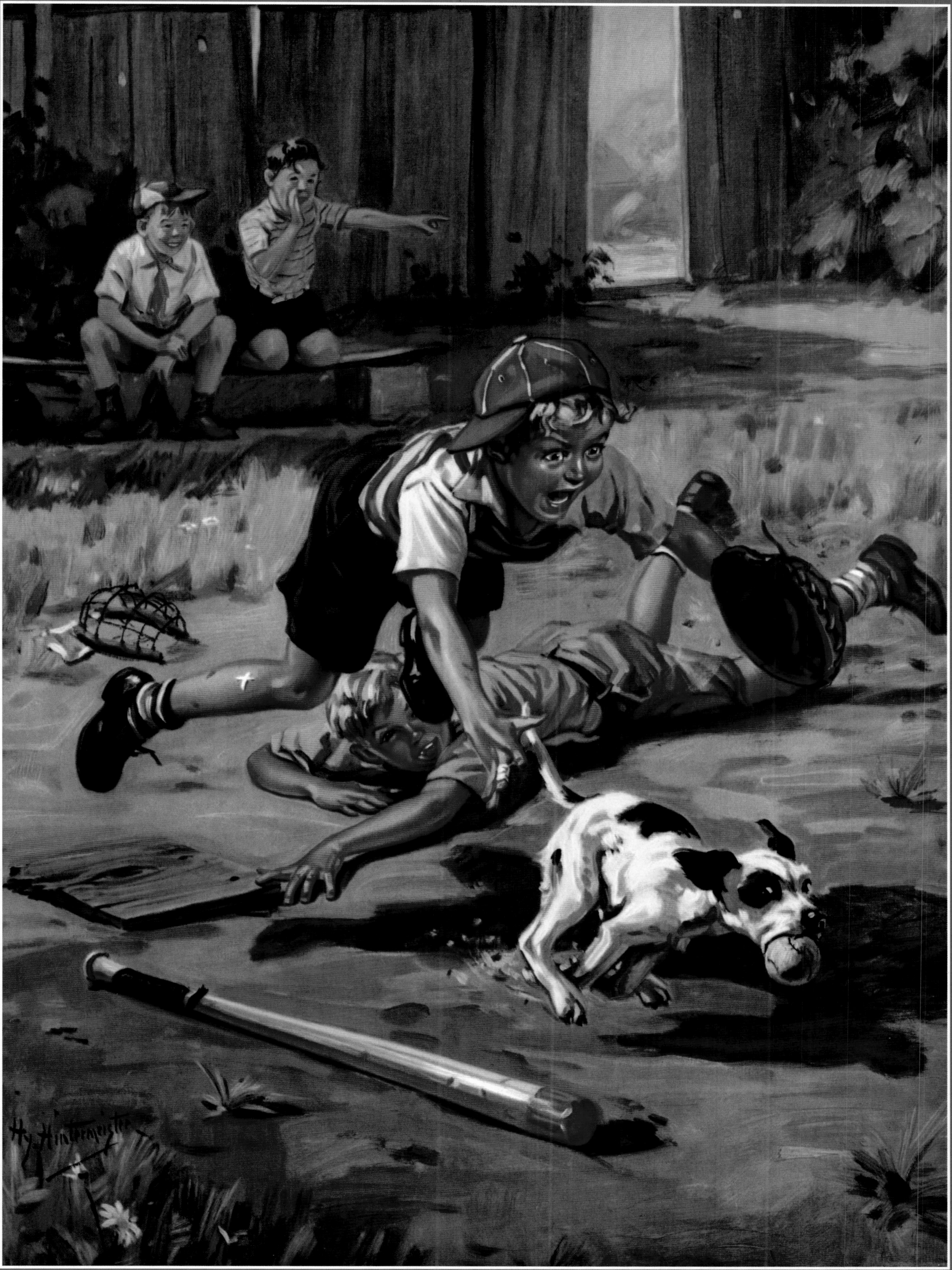
Hy Hintermeister

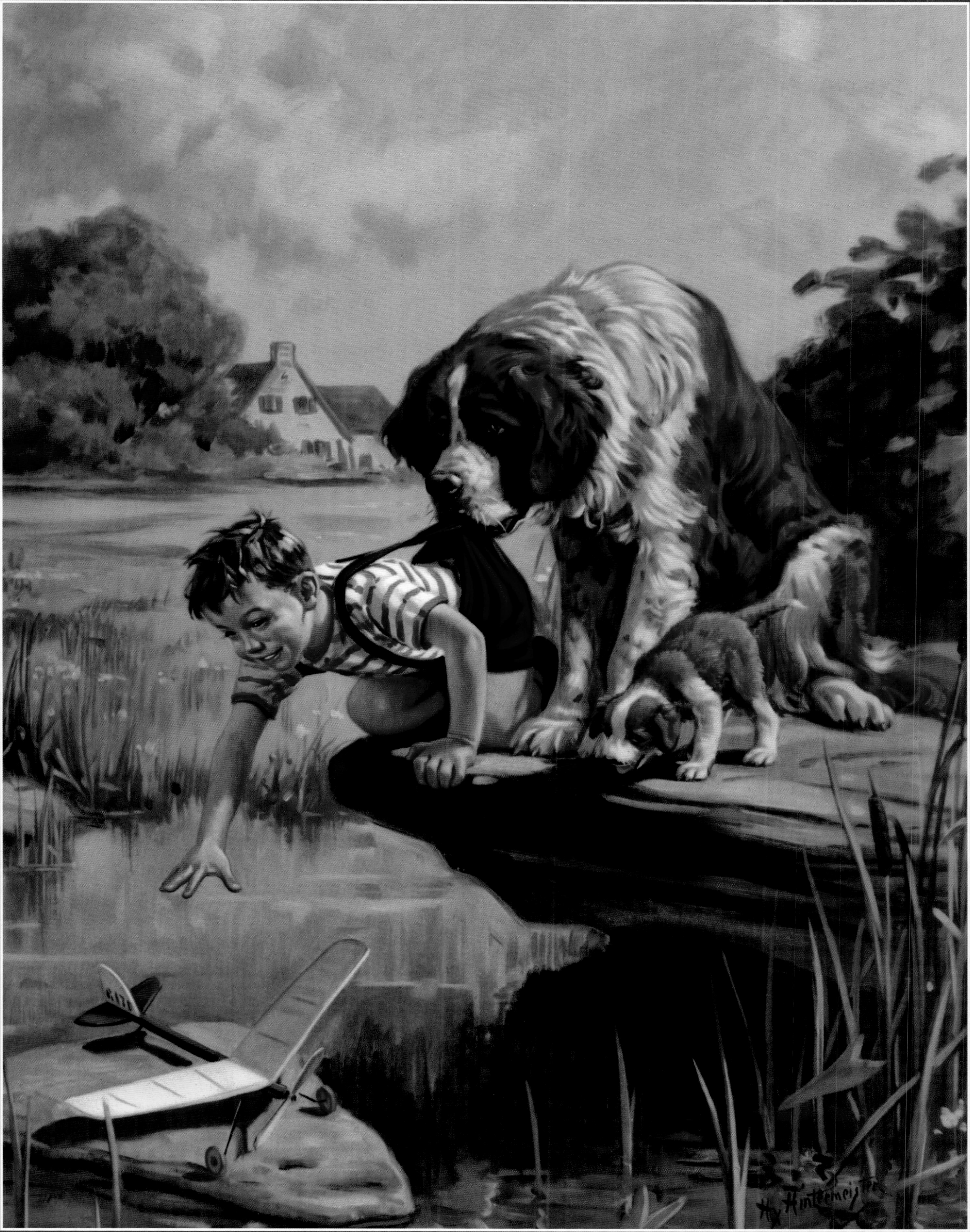

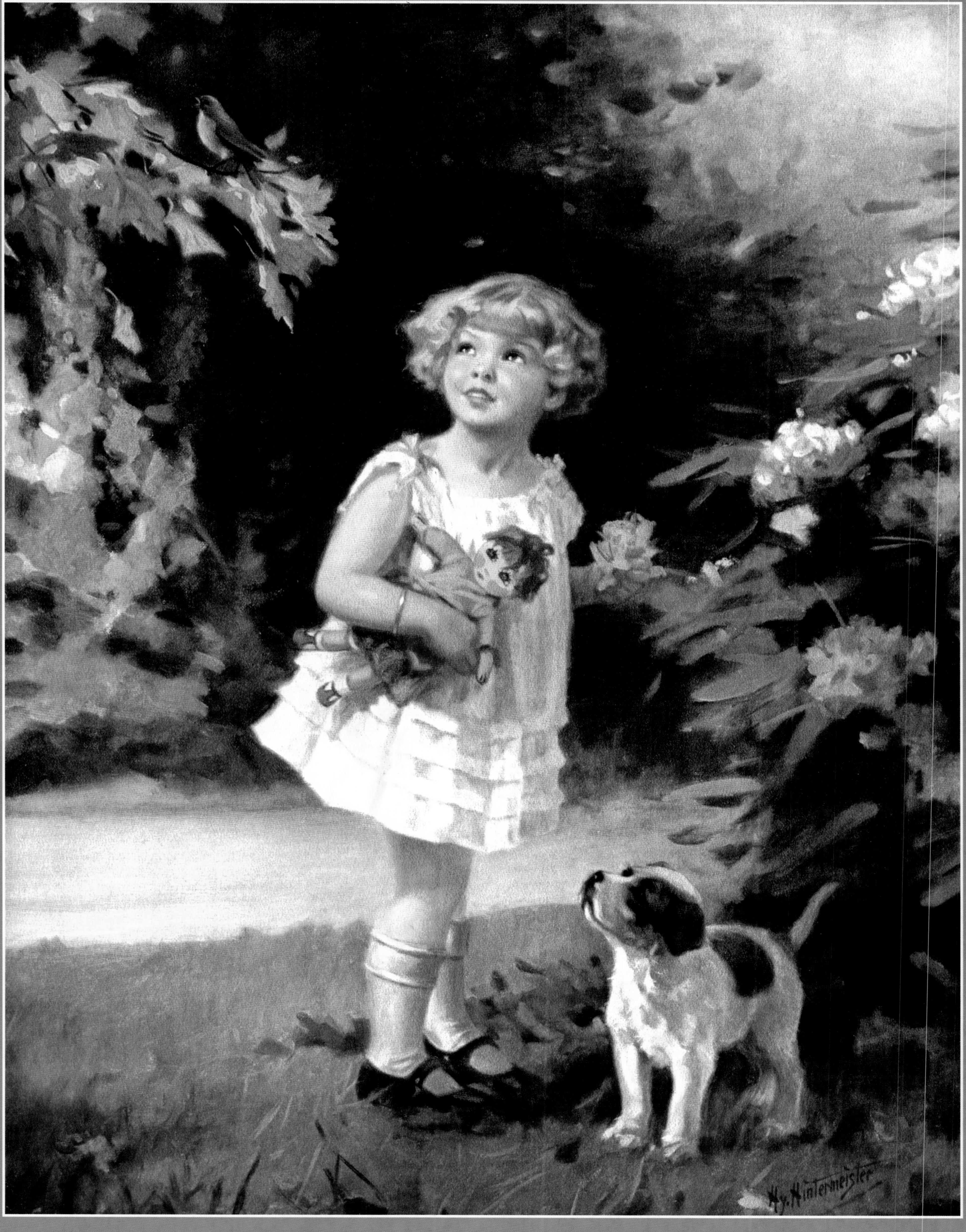
Hy. Hintermeister

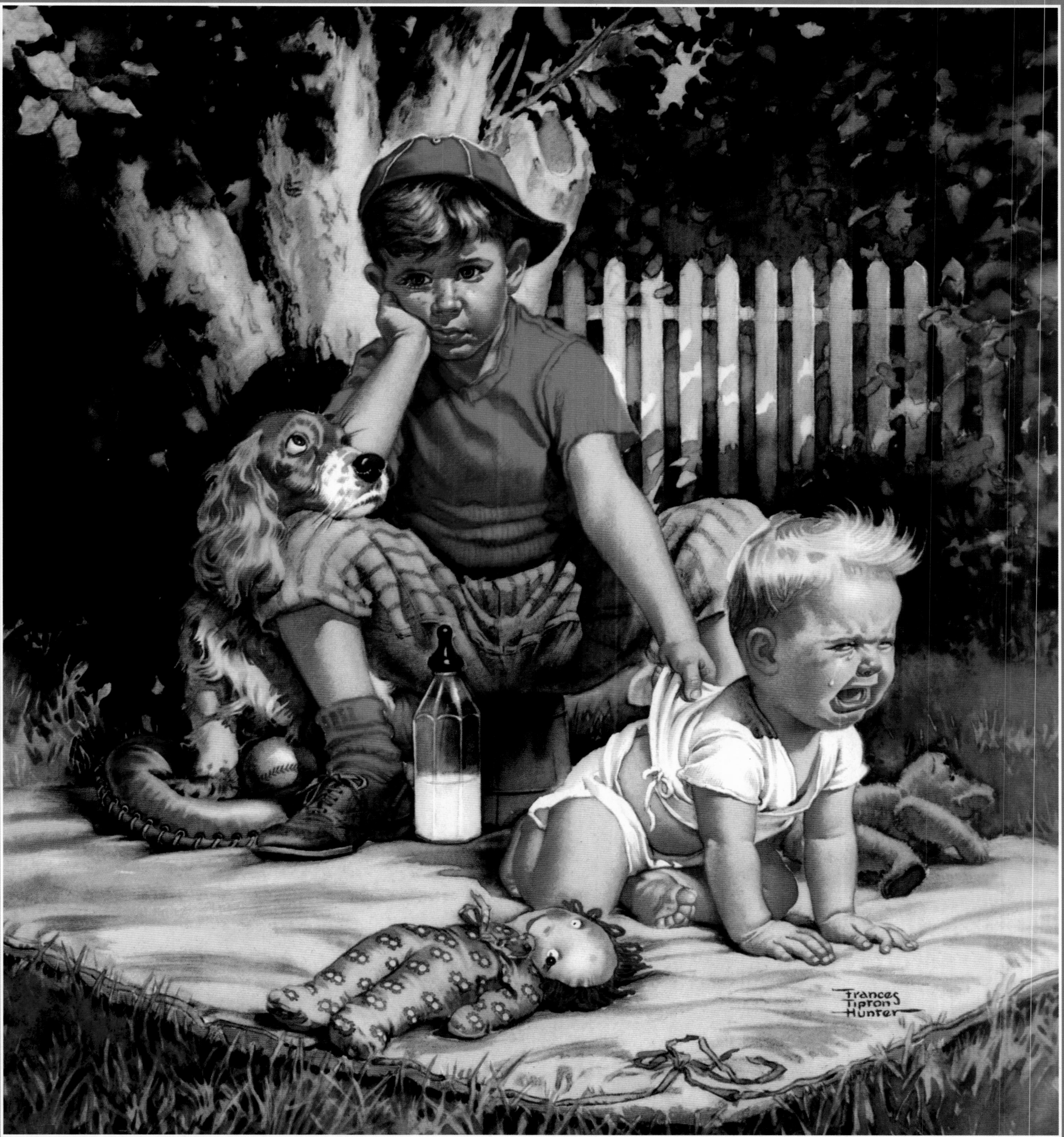
Frances Tipton Hunter

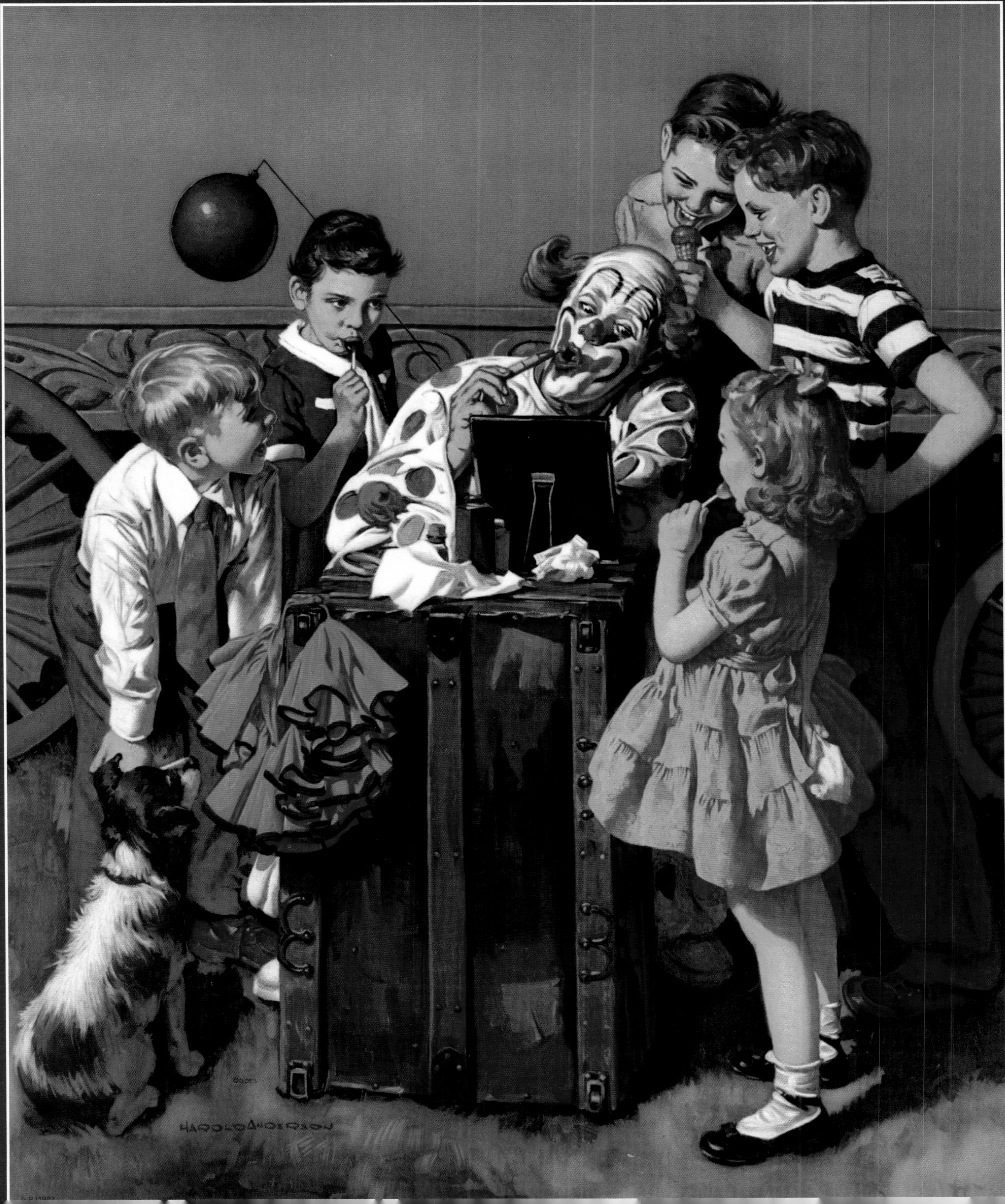
HAROLD ANDERSON

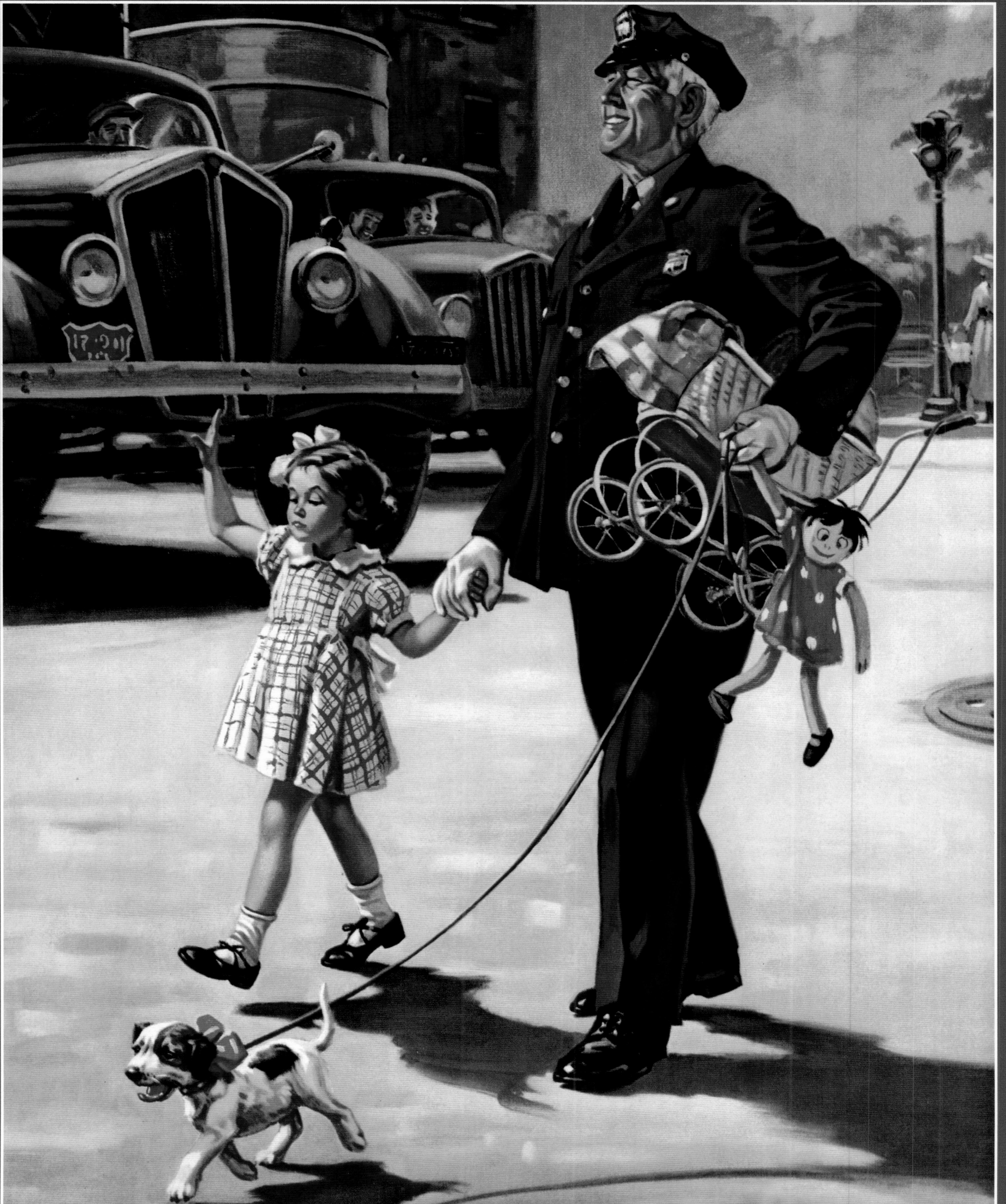

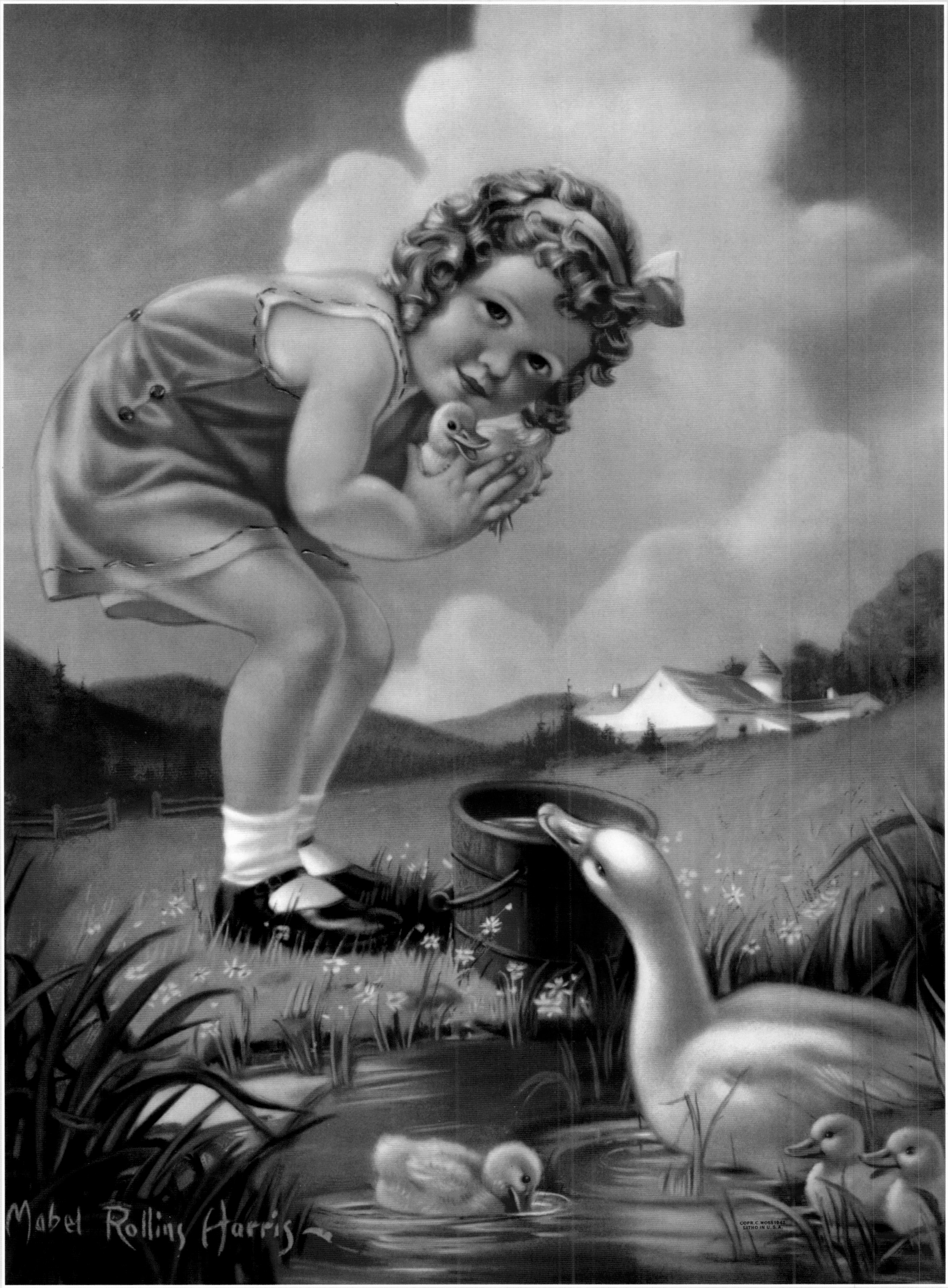
Mabel Rollins Harris
COPR. C. MOSS 1942
LITHO IN U.S.A.

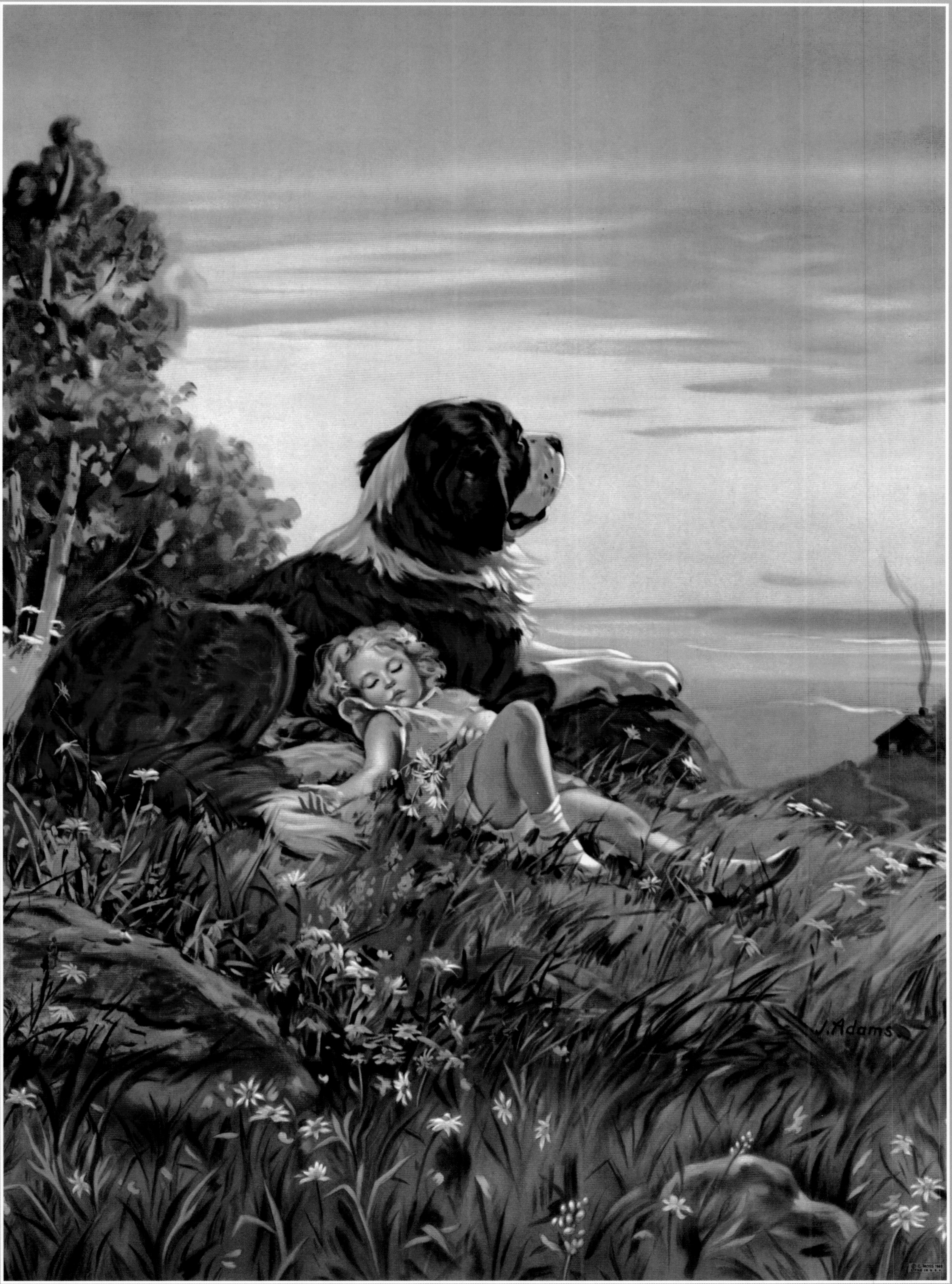
J. Adams
© C. MOSS